Rome, October 16, 1978. The white smoke signals the waiting crowds that a new Pope has been elected in the Vatican. But there's a surprise in store for the world. After four and a half centuries the Pope isn't Italian! He comes from Poland and has taken the name John Paul II.

The Youthful Years

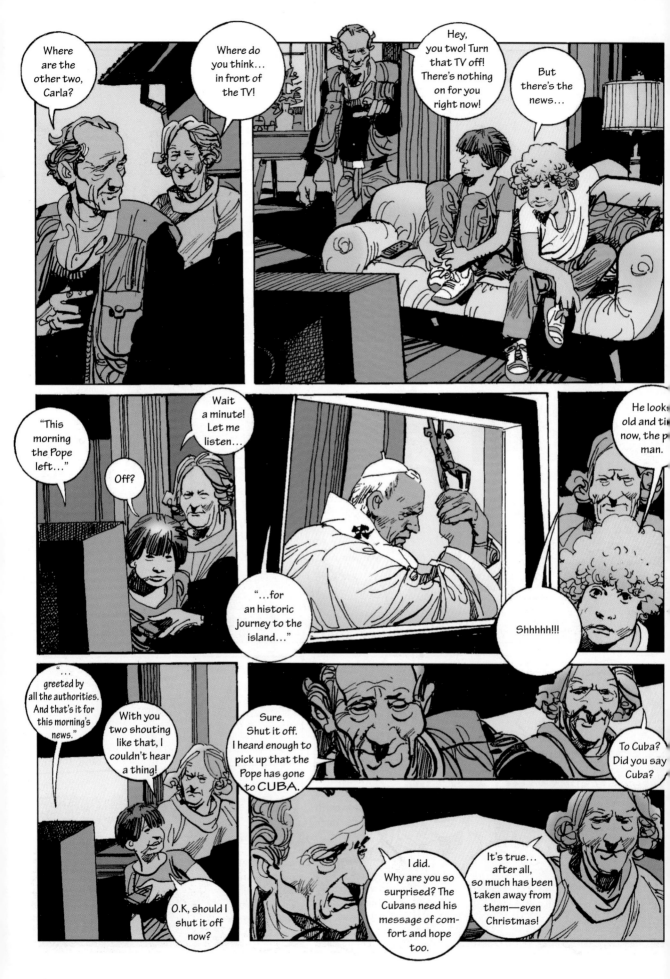

6

It's not hard at all. In fact, the answer's easy. There was nothing special or different about him.

ZAC ZAC

So?

So you should ask me why he became Pope and why I, for example, bec an engineer. There was much difference betw us in terms of our fa ily background.

I was the son of a farmer, and lived with my parents and two brothers.

Karol was the son of a non-commissioned Austro-Hungarian army officer, who later became a Polish officer. Karol lived with his parents and his brother.

No one knows what makes one person become so different from another.

I want to become a singer!

What about you, Francis?

I want to be a pilot.

I really don't know yet, but I think we're all bor liking some thing better than others.

9

11

12

13

In the Grip of War

15

18

20

21

"The Polish people rose against those who had long trodden their homeland underfoot. And the German response was violent."

"In those days Poland lived through some terrible times. Faced with the retaliation of the Soviets, the German army withdrew to its own confines and Polish soil once more became the field of bitter and bloody battles."

FEUER

Long live free Poland! Chase the foreigner out!

"The insurrection was harshly repressed and many died."

Then the Russian troops arrived and the Polish people, who thought at first that they were free again, soon realized that they'd fallen under a new domination.

But the Soviet "liberation" allowed Karol to come out of hiding and finish his studies.

He really stuck at it, didn't he!

I don't know if I could've done it.

Some people give up their goals when they meet the first obstacle, and then blame others for their failure...

Thank you, brothers, thank you. You'll always be in my heart...

...In the name of the Father, and of the Son, and of the Holy Spirit.

A few days later the young priest baptized the daughter of two old friends from the amateur theater company...

That's true, Karol. But perhaps it did say that one day you would baptize our daughter.

Halina! Tadeus! The script didn't say you should cry in this scene!

The great Director above arranges everything for our good, believe me.

By baptizing his friends' daughter, Karol showed he still had a great love for the world of acting. In that world his vocation had grown, and he remained involved in it for as long as he stayed in Poland.

What was his first job as a priest?

His first job? To pack his bags and head for Rome to study more theology at the "Angelicum" with the Dominican Fathers. It was 1946.

Finally. A break and some rest!

From Krakow
to Rome

29

His old passion for the theater and poetry, which he had never lost, resurfaced.

Did he write any plays?

Of course! One was called "The Jeweller's Shop"...

He wrote that? I remember hearing it was performed here in Italy. They even made it into a movie...

Even so, Polish Catholics knew him as a priest and scholar, not as a writer. Human rights, the rights of the family and the defense of life were the constant subjects of his teaching and preaching in the light of the Gospel.

"And so, on July 4, 1958, Pope Pius XII decided to appoint him auxiliary bishop of Krakow. At only 38, Karol was the youngest Polish bishop."

All right! He deserved it!

In 1962 he was nominated to attend the Second Vatican Council... and from 1962 to 1965 he actively participated in its meetings. He stood out as a witness of the marginalized and suffering Church in Poland, a Church that was the only bulwark of freedom behind the "Iron Curtain."*

WRRRRRRRRR

*Iron curtain: a symbolic line through Europe, which divided the states under Communist rule and those which were free and democratic.

33

Wow! What a career! He was really busy!

Yes, he was busy not only getting things done, but praying, too.

At that time something happened that was closely connected with prayer…

"Bishop Wojtyla was looking sad and worried because of some news he'd received from home."

Your Excellency, I can see you're preoccupied. Have you received some bad news?

Unfortunately, yes. It's about Wanda Poltawaska, my friend from the university. She's now a psychiatrist and has four children. They've discovered a malignant tumor in her throat. She's dying.

I'm so sorry…I wish I could do something.

All we can do is pray.

While he was praying, Karol's eye fell on a biography of Padre Pio. Karol had met him in 1946, when he was study-ing theology in Rome.

"Immediately he picked up his pen…"

"Venerable Father, I ask you to pray for a mother of four children. She's **40** years old and lives in Krakow."

"During the last war she was a prisoner in concentration camps in Germany, and now her life is threatened by cancer."

"Pray that God, through the intercession of the Blessed Virgin Mary, may show mercy to her and her family. I am deeply indebted to you. Yours in Christ, Karol Wojtyla."

Eleven days later Padre Pio received another message...

"Dear Father, I give thanks to God—and to you, Venerable Father. I must convey the greatest thanks possible on behalf of the same woman, her husband and the entire family."

What happened?

A miracle, my dear. The tumor disappeared and the lady is still alive today, enjoying full health.

Surprised, are you? Well, let's continue our story.

35

On January 18, 1964, while Vatican II was in full swing, Pope Paul VI appointed Karol Archbishop of Krakow. He was only 44!

When he put on the ancient vestments that had belonged to his medieval predecessors, Karol said…

…and remember, brothers and sisters, without the Catholic Church, Poland would never have existed!

The young archbishop held the cross high over the homeland he loved, and gave strength and hope not only to his fellow Poles, but to all those oppressed by the Soviet regime. Then, on June 26, 1967, while he was boating on Lake Mazuri…

You've done enough rowing, Tadeus. It's my turn now!

Your Excellency! Your Excellency!

Let's get in a bit closer, Tadeus. I think something's happened…

38

And 1978 was the year of the three Popes.

"In 1978 Pope Paul VI died and Pope Albino Luciani was elected, taking the name John Paul I. After his sudden death that September, the cardinals elected Karol Wojtyla Pope. He took the name John Paul II."

Three popes?

Are you sure you've got that straight, Granddad?

That means he became Pope when he was 58.

I'm sure.

On that evening of October 16, 1978, when a Polish Pope was elected, a memorable event in the Church's history took place.

What was it, Granddad?

The election of the first non-Italian Pope in almost 500 years! I can still hear those first words in his stumbling Italian.

Praised be Jesus Christ. My dear brothers and sisters, we have all bee[n] greatly saddened by the death of o[ur] beloved Pope John Paul I. And now the[se em]inent cardinals have called a new Bish[op of] Rome. They have called him from a f[ar] away country...far away, but alwa[ys] very close, through the communio[n] of faith and a shared Christian tradition.

Exactly. But there's something else about this election that's more important.

"When he became Pope, John Paul II looked out onto a world shaken by many troubles: war, hunger, underdevelopment, opposing ideologies that caused divisions and sacrificed many lives. There was the Third World with its unresolved problems, and in Europe the eyesore of the Berlin Wall…"

Pilgrim
of
Peace

48

"This was the first of many sufferings that during the course of the years forced him to undergo surgery."

"Seven months after the assassination attempt the Pope went to visit Agca in prison, bringing closure to a sad event with an act of Christian reconciliation."

If only everyone could be like that! So many people want revenge or become violent at the slightest offense!

You're right, Barbara, there's so much to learn...it shows how violence can be overcome by a simple act of love.

"Once his wounds had healed, the Pope immediately continued his mission of peace. He invited all young people of the world to come to Rome for a special Jubilee in April 1984. 250,000 answered his call!"

...follow the example of Jesus. In his name you will be able to prepare a future that is more peaceful, more human for you and your brothers and sisters. It is up to you to consecrate to him the Third Millennium which is already on the horizon.

Wow!!

Quiet!

Remember that, now!

Listen, Carla, I hope we're not going to stay inside all morning watching TV...

...the ecumenism of the Pope reaches to the very end of the earth, even to those countries where Christians are a small minority.

All right, Robert...get the portable television and let's go outside.

...when the Pope visited King Hassan II in Morocco, he told the young Muslims who had gathered in the Casablanca stadium...

...I believe that we, Christians and Muslims, must recognize with joy the religious values we have in common, and give thanks to God for them.

We both believe in one God, who is the fullness of justice and the fullness of mercy.

We must respect each other and urge each other to work for good on our way to God. Christian-Muslim dialogue must progress towards a true collaboration to ensure the mutual respect of freedom of conscience and of worship and to make sure that everyone is treated equally wherever they live.

…it does mean that all religions can come together and work together on a common task, on an earthly project which in a sense goes beyond them…every human being must follow their just conscience as they strive to obey the truth.

"Not one of the religious leaders gathered in the city of St. Francis disagreed with this message of peace, given by the Catholic Church through the Pope."

"But the Pope had chosen to preach to a much wider audience than those gathered in the Basilica at Assisi or St. Peter's Square. His audience was the entire planet!"

I want to reach all those who pray, from the Bedouin in the desert to the Carmelite or the sister in her convent…

…to those who are active and at the very height of their powers…

…to the sick on their bed of suffering…

"It wasn't any army with its nuclear threats which brought the Iron Curtain down. It wasn't any political strategy…

…but the work of unarmed and courageous men. It wasn't NATO with its missiles, but a fearless Catholic union that carried images of Mary and used the rosary as its weapon!"

SOLIDARNOŚĆ

And so the faith of a Pope "from a faraway country" swept away the Communist empire and, without violence, ended the horror of bloodshed.

A miracle! Have you seen how something that for years was considered only a dream finally became a reality?

"This wave of freedom swept everything before it and led to an event that would have been unthinkable a few years earlier. Mikhail Gorbachev, president of the crumbling Soviet Union, went to see the Pope. The world was at first astonished and then moved."

"And so this different Pope was the first, from the time of the French Revolution to the Second Vatican Council, to view and live Catholicism as a world-wide mission, one capable of changing the face of the earth."

…all you who have already the great good fortune to believe, all you who are searching for God, and even you who are tormented by doubts, I tell you, do not be afraid to accept Christ and his power! It is not that an old world is dying, but that a new one is being born!

My grandchildren! …I think they've understood…

This Pope, formed in solitude and suffering, has faced the world bravely and come out covered with wounds. Suffering has worn down his champion's constitution…

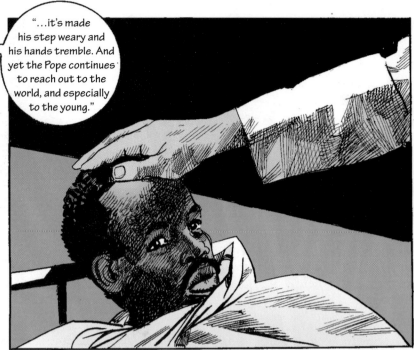

"…it's made his step weary and his hands tremble. And yet the Pope continues to reach out to the world, and especially to the young."

Which country is that?

Sssh! Let me listen.

Your task is an immense one, to overcome all evil with good, trying always in the midst of life's difficulties to place your trust in God.

Rather than in the words of the many self-interested messiahs of today who appear out of nowhere…

And you young people must oppose any form of hatred with the invincible power of Christ's love…

…this means you must be workers of peace and must build the peace of Christ's kingdom!

Never forget that, kids! It's up to you to build a better world and a better future.

Young people are his great hope! Ev[er]y time he invited them thousands came to meet in Buenos Aires, Santia[go] Compostella, Czestoch[owa] Denver, Manila, Paris, R[ome] and Toronto!

Important Events in the Life of Karol Wojtyla, Pope John Paul II

■ **May 18, 1920**

Karol Józef Wojtyla, son of Karol Wojtyla and Emilia Kaczorowska, is born at Wadowice, Poland, near the city of Kraków. He is baptized on June 20. He lives with his parents at 2 Rynek Street (today called Koszielna Street).

■ **April 13, 1929**

His mother dies.

■ **June 1930**

He begins classes at the Marcin Wadowita junior high school.

■ **December 5, 1932**

His brother Edmund dies.

■ **1934–1938**

He performs with the student drama club of Wadowice. At school he's president of the Marian Sodality. He also makes his first pilgrimage to the shrine of Our Lady of Czestochowa during this period.

■ **August 1938**

Karol and his father move to Kraków, where Karol begins studies at the Jagiellonian University and joins "Studio 38," a group of actors.

■ **September 1, 1939**

World War II begins.

■ **February 18, 1941**

Karol's father dies suddenly and Karol is left alone. In March he begins working in a stone quarry at Zakrzèwek. He and a friend start a theater group in Kraków.

■ **October 1942**

He is accepted as a seminarian of the Archdiocese of Kraków. Because of the political situation in Poland, everything must be done in secret, including his theology studies at the Jagiellonian University. Soon Karol is transferred from the stone quarry to the Solvay factory.

■ **November 1, 1946**

Karol is ordained a priest by Archbishop Adam Sapieha.

■ **November 26, 1946**

He arrives in Rome to continue his education and is enrolled at the "Angelicum."

■ **June 1948**

He receives his doctoral degree and returns to Poland.

■ **July 1948**

Father Karol serves as assistant pastor in the country parish at Niegowic.

■ **August 1949**

He is assigned as assistant pastor of St. Florian's Church in Kraków.

■ **October 1953**

He begins teaching ethics at the Jagiellonian University.

■ **December 1, 1956**

Father Karol becomes a professor of ethics at the Catholic University of Lublin. He will hold this post until he is elected Pope on October 16, 1978.

■ **July 4, 1958**

Father Karol is ordained auxiliary bishop of Kraków.

■ **October 5, 1962**

He leaves for Rome to take part in the Second Vatican Council, which begins on October 11.

■ **December 5–15, 1963**

He goes on a pilgrimage to the Holy Land with some bishops from different countries who are attending the Council.

■ **January 18, 1964**

He is named Archbishop of Kraków by Pope Paul VI.

■ **June 28, 1967**

Archbishop Wojtyla is made a cardinal by Pope Paul VI.

■ **March 7–13, 1976**

Cardinal Wojtyla preaches the Lenten retreat to Pope Paul VI and his collaborators at the Vatican.

■ **October 16, 1978 (at about 5:15 P.M.)**

Cardinal Karol Wojtyla is elected Pope and takes the name of John Paul II. He becomes the 263rd successor of St. Peter!

■ **May 13, 1981**

In an assassination attempt, Pope John Paul is shot by Ali Agca in St. Peter's Square.

■ **March 25, 1983**

The Pope opens the Holy Year of the Redemption.

■ **December 27, 1983**

Pope John Paul visits Ali Agca in prison.

■ **March 31, 1985**

He publishes the Apostolic Letter, "To the Youth of the World."

■ **April 13, 1986**

He visits the Synagogue of Rome where he meets with members of the Jewish community.

■ **October 27, 1986**

At Assisi Pope John Paul presides at the World Day of Prayer and Fasting

Karol at 18, when he was a member of the "Studio 38" theater group.

Cardinal Wojtyla in 1978, speaking at a convention in Milan, Italy.

At left and above: Pope John Paul among young people on August 19, 2000, during the 15th World Youth Day held in Rome.

The closing of the Holy Door in St. Peter's on January 6, 2001.

for Peace. Many representatives of the world religions attend.

■ June 6, 1987
He opens the special Marian Year in St. Peter's Square.

■ July 12, 1992
He is admitted to Gemelli Hospital for removal of an intestinal tumor.

■ December 7, 1992
Publication of the new *Catechism of the Catholic Church.*

■ November 14, 1994
Pope John Paul publishes the Apostolic Letter, *On Preparation for the Jubilee of the Year 2000.* In it he explains that the Catholic Church celebrates the year 2000 in a special way because it marks the 2,000th anniversary of the birth of Jesus, the Son of God. The Pope also says that the Catholic Church needs to remember and ask forgiveness for all the times in history when her members haven't followed and lived the Gospel of Jesus.

■ July 10, 1995
The Pope publishes the *Letter to Women* for the International Year of the Woman.

■ March 16, 1998
A letter written by Pope John Paul is included in the Holy See's document *We Remember: A Reflection on the Shoah.* This document is about the

Holocaust, the terrible event during which millions of European Jews and certain others were killed by the Nazis during World War II.

■ December 24, 1999
Pope John Paul begins the celebration of the Great Jubilee of the Year 2000 by opening the Holy Door of the Basilica of St. Peter.

■ February 24, 2000
He makes a jubilee pilgrimage to Mount Sinai in Egypt.

■ March 12, 2000
The Pope leads the celebration of the Day of Pardon in the Basilica of St. Peter, asking God to forgive the past sins of members of the Catholic Church.

■ March 20, 2000
Pope John Paul makes a jubilee pilgrimage to the Holy Land.

■ May 12–13, 2000
He travels to Fatima, Portugal. There he beatifies Francesco and Jacinta Marto, two of the young shepherds to whom the Blessed Virgin Mary appeared in 1913. (Beatification is a step in the process of naming someone a saint.)

■ August 15–20, 2000
In Rome the Pope celebrates the 15th World Youth Day with young people from all across the globe. More than two million of them attend the final Mass!

■ January 6, 2001
Pope John Paul closes the Holy Door of St. Peter's Basilica, marking the end of the Great Jubilee of the Year 2000.

■ May 4–8, 2001
The Pope makes a pilgrimage to Greece, Syria and Malta, traveling in the footsteps of St. Paul. In Athens he meets with Archbishop Christodoulos and other leaders and members of the Greek Orthodox Church. In Damascus he meets with Muslim religious leaders and becomes the first Pope ever to enter a mosque.

■ July 25–28, 2002
Pope John Paul celebrates the 17th World Youth Day in Toronto, Canada with thousands of young people from around the globe.

■ July 29–31, 2002
Pope John Paul travels to Mexico City, Mexico for the canonization of Blessed Juan Diego.

Pope John Paul II's Pastoral Visits around the World

1979

1 January 25—February 1
Dominican Republic,
Mexico, Bahamas

2 June 2–10
Poland

3 September 29—October 8
Ireland, USA

4 November 28–30
Turkey

1980

5 May 2–12
Zaire, Congo, Kenya,
Ghana, Burkina Faso, Ivory
Coast

6 May 30—June 2
France

7 June 30—July 12
Brazil

8 November 15–19
Germany

1981

9 February 16–27
Pakistan, Philippines, USA
(Guam and Anchorage),
Japan

1982

10 February 12–19
Nigeria, Benin, Gabon,
Equatorial Guinea

11 May 12–15
Portugal

12 May 28—June 2
Great Britain

13 June 10–13
Argentina and Brazil

14 June 15
Switzerland

15 August 28
San Marino

16 October 28—November 9
Spain

1983

17 March 2–10
Portugal, Costa Rica,
Nicaragua, Panama,
El Salvador, Guatemala,
Haiti, Honduras, Belize

18 June 16–25
Poland

19 August 14–15
Lourdes, France

20 September 10–13
Austria

POLAND 1979

MEXICO 1979

PAPUA NEW GUINEA 1984

UNITED STATES 1987

AUSTRALIA 1986

MADAGASCAR 1989

SPAIN 1989

RWANDA 1990

40 October 8–11
France

1989

41 April 28—May 6
Madagascar, Reunion, Zambia, Malawi

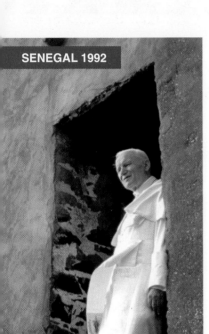
SENEGAL 1992

42 June 1–10
Norway, Iceland, Finland, Denmark, Sweden

43 August 19–21
Spain

44 October 6–16
South Korea, Indonesia, Mauritius

1990

45 January 25—February 1
Cape Verde, Guinea-Bissau, Mali, Chad, Burkina Faso

46 April 21–22
Czechoslovakia

47 May 6–14
Mexico

48 May 25–27
Curaçao, Malta

49 September 1–10
Tanzania, Burundi, Rwanda, Ivory Coast

1991

50 May 10–13
Portugal

51 June 1–9
Poland

52 August 13–20
Poland, Hungary

53 October 12–21
Brazil

1992

54 February 19–26
Senegal, Gambia, Guinea

55 June 4–10
Angola, Sao Tomé, Principe (Prince Island)

56 October 9–14
Dominican Republic

1993

57 February 3–10
Uganda, Sudan, Benin

ANGOLA 1992

LITHUANIA 1993

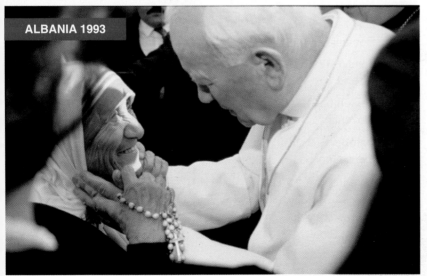
ALBANIA 1993

58 April 25
Albania

59 June 12–17
Spain

60 August 9–16
Jamaica, Mexico, USA

61 September 4–10
Lithuania, Latvia, Estonia

1994

62 September 10–11
Croatia

1995

63 January 11–21
Philippines, Papua New
Guinea, Australia, Sri Lanka

64 May 20–22
Czech Republic, Poland

65 June 3–4
Belgium

66 June 30—July 3
Slovakia

67 September 14–20
Cameroon, Republic of
South Africa, Kenya

68 October 4–9
USA

1996

69 February 5–12
Guatemala, Nicaragua,
El Salvador, Venezuela

70 April 14
Tunisia

71 May 17–18
Slovenia

72 June 21–23
Germany

73 September 6–7
Hungary

74 September 19–22
France

1997

75 April 12–13
Bosnia-Herzegovina

SLOVENIA 1996

76 April 25–27
Czech Republic

77 May 10–11
Lebanon

78 May 31—June 10
Poland

79 August 21–24
France

80 October 2–6
Brazil

1998

81 January 21–26
Cuba

82 March 21–23
Nigeria

83 June 19–21
Austria

84 October 2–4
Croatia

1999

85 January 22–28
Mexico, USA

86 May 7–9
Romania

87 June 5–17
Poland

88 September 19
Slovenia

89 October 5–9
India, Georgia

2000

90 February 24–26
Egypt, Sinai

CUBA 1998

91 March 20–26
Jordan, Israel

92 May 12–13
Portugal

2001

93 May 4–9
Greece, Syria, Malta

94 June 23–27
Ukraine

95 September 22–27
Kazakhstan, Armenia

2002

96 May 22–26
Azerbaijan, Bulgaria

97 July 25–31
Canada, Mexico